First paperback edition 2022
Book illustrations by Kavion Robinson

ISBN 978-1-7376080-4-2

Publisher Unabashed Kids Media
UnabashedKids.com

www.unabashedkids.com

My earliest memory of my father is of him working out by the front door of our home. He would do push-ups in front of the door. One day I climbed onto his back and began to count, just like Angela.

- Author Kerice Robinson

Dad Is My Best Friend

Words by: Kerice K. Robinson
Pictures by: Kavion Robinson

Hi! My name is Angela.

This is a story about me and my dad.

He is my best friend.

I have other friends

My mom is my friend

The kids on the playground
are my friends too.

My dad is like no other friend.
He is my **BEST** friend.

We do everything together!

We even exercise together, to keep
our muscles strong.

I ride my bike with my dad.

Dad says

"Ready! Set! Go!"

I peddle as fast as I can.
He comes running behind me.
He always catches up to me.

I race my dad.

Dad says
"Ready! Set! Go!"

Dad runs with me. He is super fast.
Sometimes I win. Sometimes Dad wins.
But, we jump and celebrate, no
matter who wins.

We do push-ups together.
Dad says

"Ready! Set! Go!"

I do as many as I can until I get tired.

Then dad does push-ups.
I watch and count.

Some days, I lay on his back while
I count.

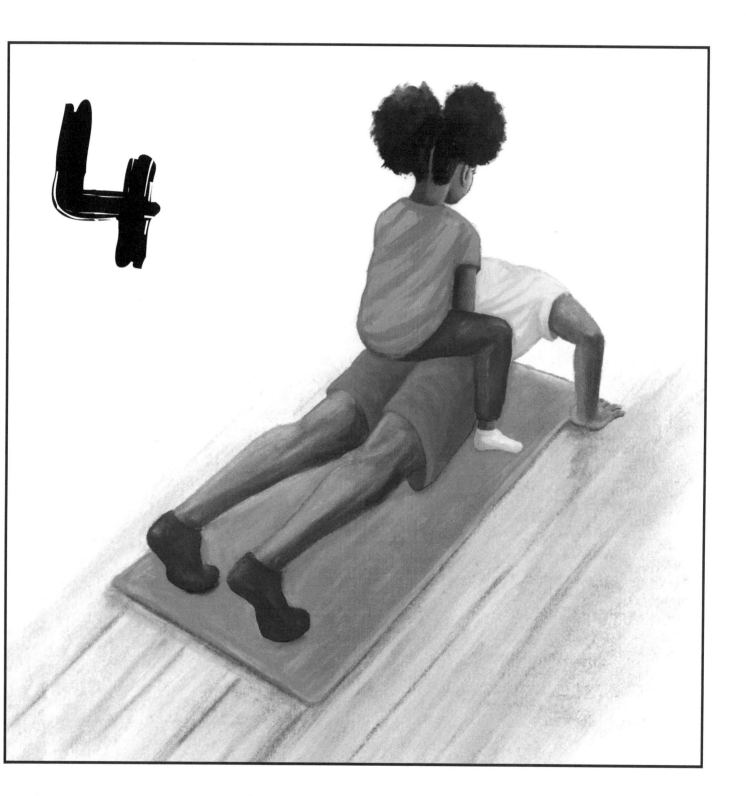

5

I write down how many push-ups dad can do with me on his back.

Today he did 10.
A new record!

Last week he did 8, that was the old record.

After a long day of playing with my best friend.

When all of the races have finished. When the sun has set. When the moon comes out. When the stars shine bright.

When we both are tired, Dad tucks me into my warm cozy bed. He reads me a story and kisses me goodnight.

Then he says

"I love you."

CPSIA information can be obtained
at www.ICGtesting.com
Printed in the USA
LVHW071123260522
719791LV00002B/52